·RAVEN and the SUN·

echoing our ancestors

ADAPTED BY

NOELLE M.K.Y. KAHANU

ILLUSTRATED BY

HARINANI ORME

KAMAHOI
PRESS

Nā moʻolelo no nā pua ʻalamea
Stories for our precious children.

Kamahoi describes delight or fascination and a sense of wonder or awe. The parts of the word add special connotation, in that "kama" refers to people, especially children, and "hoi" denotes interest. As a title for the young people's book series, Kamahoi carries many positive attributes, and embodies the goals of this publishing effort.

Kamahoi Press is a division of the Bishop Museum Press.

BISHOP MUSEUM PRESS
1525 BERNICE STREET
HONOLULU, HAWAIʻI 96817

ISBN-10: 1-58178-067-2
ISBN-13: 978-1-58178-067-3

BOOK DESIGN BY JULIE CHUN

Printed in Korea

Library of Congress Cataloging-in-Publication Data
Kahanu, Noelle M.K.Y.
Raven and the sun : echoing our ancestors / Noelle M.K.Y. Kahanu; illustrations by Harinani Orme.
p. cm.
"ECHO: Education through Cultural and Historical Organizations"--T.p. verso.
ISBN 1-58178-067-2 (hardcover : alk. paper)
1. Indian mythology--Juvenile literature. 2. Creation--Mythology--Juvenile literature. 3. Indians of North America--Folklore. 4. Alaska--Folklore. 5. Hawaii--Folklore. 6. Massachusetts--Folklore. I. Orme, Harinani, ill. II. Education through Cultural and Historical Organizations (Project) III. Title.

E59.R38K35 2007
398.20973--dc22
2007000184

IN FEBRUARY OF 2006, EIGHT STORYTELLERS from Alaska, Hawai'i, and Massachusetts gathered on the windswept shoreline of Kualoa, O'ahu. For two weeks they worked together, weaving their songs and stories of creation, light, and life—giving voice to the oral histories of their ancestors. Through their creative efforts was born the play "Listen to the Stories," upon which this book is based. Within these pages are the stories of the Iñupiat and Yup'ik people of Alaska, the Native people of Hawai'i, and the Wampanoags of Martha's Vineyard. Each time a story is shared, whether spoken, written, dreamed, or remembered, it is a gift—from those who came before to those who carry on in their footsteps. Thank you to each of these storytellers for enabling us to share these gifts with future generations.

RAVEN GAVE THE WORLD LIGHT AND WATER and many other things—but he is also a rascal who likes to trick people. Raven especially likes to play tricks on the Sun.

Many people around the world have different stories about how light and the Sun came into being.

At the time when the earth was heated, at the time when the heavens turned about, born was Kumulipo in the night, a male; born was Pōʻele in the night, a female.

In Hawai'i, Hawaiians believe that life emerged from darkness. From the depths of the sea was born the very first life forms. Over time, life increased in the ocean, on land, and in the sky. Light was born and burst forth.

In Alaska, the Iñupiat people of Point Hope tell how the great hunter, Tuluniġraq, ended their darkness. One day Tuluniġraq headed east in search of light. After three days, he came upon an iglu and peeked through an ice window.

Inside, he saw a father working on his hunting gear, a mother mending winter clothes and a young girl playing. Tuluniġraq also saw three spheres hanging from the wall: one was very bright, one was not so bright, and one was dim.

"Papa, can I play with the brightest ball?" asked the little girl.

"Naumi—no," said her father. She begged him again, and when their backs were turned,
Tuluniġraq swooped in and took the two spheres that were not so bright.

He tossed one into the sky, and it became the moon. He tossed the other, and it shattered into a million pieces that flew into the night sky, becoming the stars.

There was now only the brightest ball left. "Please, Papa, can I play with it?"

"Yes," sighed her father. Happily, the little girl took the ball and tossed it into the air, but it fell to the floor and rolled near the door.

Tuluniġraq saw his chance and grabbed the ball! He fled home to Point Hope where he released the sphere into the sky, thus bringing light to his people.

"I remember that!" says the Sun. "I'm so glad I'm no longer trapped in that ball. I am the light and the light is me, the sun, the moon, and the stars! Everyone is in love with me!"

"Don't get so full of yourself," replies Raven. "Remember you are not the center of the universe in all cultures! Some stories don't even include you, like the story of Moshup and how he created the island of Noepe."

Moshup was a beloved giant of the Wampanoag people who would travel to a place called Noepe.
There, near white clay cliffs, he would catch whales to feed his people.

Moshup, dashing the whales against the cliffs, would then cook them over fire. Eventually, the color of the cliffs changed to hues of red, white, black, and yellow.

Moshup decided to protect his people by leading them to Noepe where they could live peacefully. On the journey he dragged his feet, causing large grooves to form in the earth.

The ocean rushed to fill these spaces, surrounding the high areas and separating Noepe from the mainland. This is how the island of Noepe, now called Martha's Vineyard in Massachusetts, was created.

"Yes, but I am in many other stories," says Sun. "After all, I am the brightest being in the Universe!"
"Hmmm," muses Raven, "I seem to recall a story from Hawai'i where you really got cut down to size with Māui's magical adze."

"Māui," his mother called, "look at my kapa. It is still damp! The sun is racing too fast across the sky and my bark cloth won't dry. Please slow him down for me. Go see your grandmother, and she will help you."

Māui made the long journey to see his grandmother. She gave him a braid of her hair, from which to weave a magical rope. "Hide upon the highest mountain," she said, "and when the sun first rises, capture him with this rope!"

The next morning, as the Sun rose, Māui lassoed it with his rope. "Release me!" cried the Sun.

"Only if you promise to slow down," said Māui. The Sun promised, but then he suddenly tried to escape!
Wielding his magical adze, Māui chopped off the Sun's rays. To this day, the Sun now hobbles slowly across the sky.

"Ouch!" says the Sun. "Did you really have to bring that story up? I'm really not that bad. And don't forget, I am the moonlight, too. Can't you think of a nicer story?"

"Well," says Raven, "there is a beautiful Yup'ik song I remember hearing long ago. It goes something like this..."

Nighttime is coming. Darkness is spreading across the land. But our ancestors are in the moon looking down on us, with their rays of hope. They are lighting our land so beautifully.

"What wonderful stories we have shared," say Raven and the Sun. "By retelling them, we keep them alive! Listen to the stories of your elders, and those in your family and community.

These stories will help you to always remember who you are and where you come from—for in them, you can hear the echoes of your ancestors."

BACKGROUND INFORMATION

Raven and the Sun: Echoing our Ancestors shares creation tales of the Native peoples of Alaska,
Hawai'i, and Massachusetts. Read below to learn more about these people and where they come from.

IÑUPIAT PEOPLE OF NORTHERN ALASKA

The Iñupiat people live along the northern slope of Alaska. They have thrived for thousands of years in one of the harshest climates on Earth, hunting the bowhead whale, which they call "Aġviq." They continue to subsist largely on the land and sea, their lives revolving around the whale, walrus, seal, polar bear, caribou, and fish. To the people of the north, the extreme climate is not a barrier, but a natural realm for a variety of mammals, birds, and fish, gathered by the people for survival.

NATIVE HAWAIIAN PEOPLE OF HAWAI'I

Within the Pacific Ocean are the Hawaiian Islands, the most isolated archipelago in the world. Native Hawaiians believe that man, and even the gods, came from a place called Kahiki, journeying thousands of miles to arrive in Hawai'i. To Hawaiians, all things have life, value, and are related in a complex genealogy of the world, as evidenced by the "Kumulipo," an ancient chant that connects all beings, from ocean creatures, to birds, plants, animals, and man.

YUP'IK PEOPLE OF SOUTHWEST ALASKA

The people of the Yup'ik culture live along the coast and rivers of Southwest Alaska. They depend largely upon subsistence fishing, hunting both land and sea mammals, and gathering berries and roots for food, as have their ancestors for thousands of years. Elders tell stories of the traditional ways of life as a way to teach younger generations about their heritage and to pass on skills necessary for survival.

WAMPANOAG TRIBE OF GAY HEAD

The ancestors of Wampanoag people have lived for at least 10,000 years at Aquinnah (Gay Head) and throughout the island of Noepe (Martha's Vineyard), pursuing a traditional economy based on fishing and agriculture. The Aquinnah Wampanoag share the belief that the giant Moshup created Noepe and the neighboring islands, taught their people how to fish and to catch whales, and still presides over their destinies. Their beliefs and a hundred million years of history are imprinted in the colorful clay cliffs of Aquinnah.

SUGGESTED STORYTELLING ACTIVITIES

In the Western world today, the word "story" is often not taken seriously. But stories are more than fables and fairy tales; they are essential parts of the human experience that help explain the world around us. They can also be about real people and places. Through stories, we learn about ourselves—our histories, our families, and communities. We learn about other people and what is important to them. Each story is a unique gift, for everyone receives something different and very personal from each story he or she hears. With these activities below, maybe someday you, too, can become a storyteller, and share your gifts with the world.

- There are many different ways to tell a story. A story can be told through pictures and writing, as in this book, and a story can also be told through song, dance, and drama. Choose one of the stories in this book and present it to a friend or family member in a new way.

- The stories in this book were passed down from generation to generation. You can ask elders in your family and community to pass along stories they know. Ask them to tell stories about special people they know, places that are important to them, significant life events, and memorable objects they own. Practice telling these stories back to them, or write them down, so that you can remember them too.

- Both Raven and Maui are trickster figures, using their wiles to play tricks on the sun. Many cultures tell stories about trickster figures. Can you think of other tricksters in stories from different cultures?

- The Wampanoag people believe that the giant Moshup created the island of Noepe. Every culture tells stories about how the world came to be. What are some other creation stories you know?

- There are also many stories of how the sun and the moon were formed. Can you think of any of these stories? Can you make up your own story about how these wondrous beings came into the world?

ACKNOWLEDGMENTS

We wish to express our deepest appreciation to the following storytellers who created the play "Listen to the Stories" in 2006, upon which this publication is based: STEPHEN BLANCHETT (Yup'ik/Inuit) of Bethel, Alaska; JACK DALTON (Yup'ik) of Hooper Bay, Alaska; KEALOHA KELEKOLIO (Hawaiian) of Mākaha, Hawai'i; JAMES QULIUQ PATKOTAK (Iñupiaq) of Barrow, Alaska; DAVE PELOQUIN of Mystic, Connecticut; TOBIAS VANDERHOOP (Wampanoag) of Gay Head (Aquinnah), Massachusetts; and MALIA YAMAMOTO of Honolulu, Hawai'i. Guiding the development of the play and providing artistic direction was PETER ROCKFORD ESPIRITU (Hawaiian) of Tau Dance Theater, a Honolulu-based professional dance company, as well as ESTHER IZUO. We wish to acknowledge the ECHO partner institutions for supporting the creation of the play and this publication: Alaska Native Heritage Center; North Slope Borough ECHO Project; Bishop Museum; New Bedford ECHO Project; and Peabody Essex Museum. To the Wampanoag Tribe of Gay Head (Aquinnah), thank you for your blessings and guidance regarding the story of Moshup. We are also indebted to KEALOHA KELEKOLIO of Bishop Museum for his assistance in the early drafts of this publication, NANCY ALI of Bishop Museum for developing the storytelling activities, RON COX of Bishop Museum Press for his expertise, leadership and support, and Native Hawaiian visual artist HARINANI ORME, whose wonderful illustrations truly brought these stories to life. And finally, we wish to give thanks to all the ancestors who first gave voice to these stories through their chants, songs, and dances of long ago.

Haʻina ʻia mai ana ka puana.
Let their stories be told.

ECHO: Education through Cultural and Historical Organizations

Education through Cultural and Historical Organizations (ECHO) is a major federally funded educational and cultural enrichment initiative that has served hundreds of thousands of children and adult continuing learners in Alaska, Hawai'i, Massachusetts, and Mississippi. Established by Congress as part of the No Child Left Behind Act of 2001, ECHO brings to culturally diverse audiences innovative programs collaboratively produced by six regional cultural entities: Alaska Native Heritage Center and the North Slope Borough ECHO Project in Alaska; Bishop Museum in Hawai'i; the New Bedford ECHO Project and Peabody Essex Museum in Massachusetts; and the Mississippi Band of Choctaw Indians.

Together, ECHO partner institutions represent more than four centuries of experience serving the educational needs of their communities. While varying in individual missions, all embrace common goals: to enhance appreciation of regional heritage, to facilitate dialogue and understanding between communities and individuals, and to provide life-enhancing educational, social, and personal development opportunities beyond those available in traditional classrooms.

This publication is funded by ECHO, which is administered by the United States Department of Education, Office of Innovation and Improvement.

www.alaskanative.net

www.echonsb.org

www.bishopmuseum.org

www.newbedfordecho.org

www.pem.org

www.choctaw.org

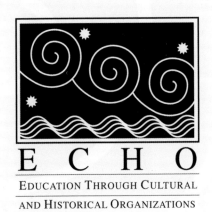

ECHO

EDUCATION THROUGH CULTURAL
AND HISTORICAL ORGANIZATIONS